Sir Squash

PHASE 5

/er/

Level 8 – Purple

Helpful Hints for Reading at Home

The graphemes (written letters) and phonemes (units of sound) used throughout this series are aligned with Letters and Sounds. This offers a consistent approach to learning whether reading at home or in the classroom.

HERE IS A LIST OF PHONEMES FOR THIS PHASE OF LEARNING. AN EXAMPLE OF THE PRONUNCIATION CAN BE FOUND IN BRACKETS.

Phase 5			
ay (day)	ou (out)	ie (tie)	ea (eat)
oy (boy)	ir (girl)	ue (blue)	aw (saw)
wh (when)	ph (photo)	ew (new)	oe (toe)
au (Paul)	a_e (make)	e_e (these)	i_e (like)
o_e (home)	u_e (rule)		

Phase 5 Alternative Pronunciations of Graphemes			
a (hat, what)	e (bed, she)	i (fin, find)	o (hot, so, other)
u (but, unit)	c (cat, cent)	g (got, giant)	ow (cow, blow)
ie (tied, field)	ea (eat, bread)	er (farmer, herb)	ch (chin, school, chef)
y (yes, by, very)	ou (out, shoulder, could, you)		

HERE ARE SOME WORDS WHICH YOUR CHILD MAY FIND TRICKY.

Phase 5 Tricky Words			
oh	their	people	Mr
Mrs	looked	called	asked
could			

TOP TIPS FOR HELPING YOUR CHILD TO READ:

- Allow children time to break down unfamiliar words into units of sound and then encourage children to string these sounds together to create the word.

- Encourage your child to point out any focus phonics when they are used.

- Read through the book more than once to grow confidence.

- Ask simple questions about the text to assess understanding.

- Encourage children to use illustrations as prompts.

PHASE 5

/er/

This book focuses on the grapheme /er/ and is a purple level 8 book band.

Sir Squash

Written by
John Wood

Illustrated by
Emre Karacan

My name is Bernard. I want to tell you about my father. He has an odd shop at the top of the street. When he is in his shop, he has his blue apron on.

My father is big and strong. If you met him, he could pick you up with one finger.

Mums, dads, brothers and sisters all come to his shop for help. There are lots of things they need help with, but each time my father helps in the same way...

… he squashes something! There is no other squasher better than my father. My father has squashed so much that he has a nickname. He is Sir Squash.

My job in the shop is to be a sweeper. I am not strong like my father. I am short and thin. But if I cannot squash things, who will be the manager after my father?

But I never had much time to think about it.
There were customers to serve.

"I have too much maths to do," said one person with a jersey. "Can you help me Sir Squash?"

"I can be of service," said Sir Squash.
Squash! Her pile of maths was squashed into
just one sheet of paper.
"Thank you. That is so much better," said
the girl. "Now I can play games sooner."

"There is a wasp! Quick, take that wasp to Sir Squash to be squashed," said a boy.
Sir Squash had no concern. He did not have to think long!

Squash! My father squashed the wasp until it was the size of a speck of dust.
"Perfect! Thank you for the help," said the boy.

A girl ran in with a bagel.
"My bagel is too big to fit in my mouth,"
she said.
After thinking hard, Sir Squash worked it out.

Soft squash! My father squashed the bagel until it was just the right size.
The girl tried to say thank you, but her mouth was full of bagel.

At the end of each day, when the customers had left, I tried to squash things. Perhaps a small object might work. But it was no good. I could not even squash a bean.

I went back to sweeping the shop and serving customers.
One day a frail man visited the shop. He was not much of a smiler.

"I need help, Sir Squash," said the man.
"You see, I just feel sad all the time."
"I am sure I can help you," said my father.

Sir Squash led the man into the shop and did what he did best. Squash!
"I still feel sad," said the man.

My father and I gasped.
"What if I did not squash right? I will
do it better this time," said my father.

My father squashed and squashed. He squashed with his hands. He squashed with a club. He jumped off the roof and squashed with his powerful bum. He squashed with whatever might he could muster.

My father was at a loss. He went outside and lay on the ground. It began to rain. "Well, that was concerning. What shall we do?" said Sir Squash.

I went back inside the shop to see the man.
"How does it feel to be sad?" I asked.
"It feels hard to get up. Like I am dragging
a stone all the time," said the man.

I patted the man on the back as he spoke.
He spoke about his sadness for a long time.
The more he spoke, the better he felt.

"I feel better now that I have spoken to you, Bernard," said the man. "My sadness has been let out. Thank you!"
The man smiled and left the shop.

"You did it, Bernard!" he said. "You helped someone feel better, and you did not even need to squash."
My father cheered and lifted me up.

"I have something for you," my father said.
We went to the back of the shop and he took
out a box. Inside was a soft, blue apron.
It was my size.

"You own the shop now," said my father.
He grabbed the broom and started to sweep,
smiling to himself.
These days, I help the customers.
But sometimes, my father still helps with
some things...

Squash! Together, there is no person that we cannot help.

Sir Squash

1. How does Sir Squash help people?

2. What does Sir Squash wear?
   (a) A red hat
   (b) A green tie
   (c) A blue apron

3. Whose problem can Sir Squash not solve?

4. How does Bernard help to solve the problem?

5. If you could squash one of your problems, what would it be?

© 2022 **BookLife Publishing Ltd.**
King's Lynn, Norfolk, PE30 4LS, UK

ISBN 978-1-80155-476-3

All rights reserved. Printed in Poland.
A catalogue record for this book is available from
the British Library.

Sir Squash
Written by John Wood
Illustrated by Emre Karacan

An Introduction to BookLife Readers...

Our Readers have been specifically created in line with the London Institute of Education's approach to book banding and are phonetically decodable and ordered to support each phase of the Letters and Sounds document.

Each book has been created to provide the best possible reading and learning experience. Our aim is to share our love of books with children, providing both emerging readers and prolific page-turners with beautiful books that are guaranteed to provoke interest and learning, regardless of ability.

BOOK BAND GRADED using the Institute of Education's approach to levelling.

PHONETICALLY DECODABLE supporting each phase of Letters and Sounds.

EXERCISES AND QUESTIONS to offer reinforcement and to ascertain comprehension.

BEAUTIFULLY ILLUSTRATED to inspire and provoke engagement, providing a variety of styles for the reader to enjoy whilst reading through the series.

AUTHOR INSIGHT:
JOHN WOOD

An incredibly creative and talented author, John Wood has written many books for BookLife Publishing. Born in Warwickshire, he graduated with a BA in English Literature and English Language from De Montfort University. During his studies, he learned about literature, styles of language, linguistic relativism, and psycholinguistics, which is the study of the effects of language on the brain. Thanks to his learnings, John successfully uses words that captivate and resonate with children and that will be sure to make them retain information. His stories are entertaining, memorable, and extremely fun to read.

PHASE 5

/er/

This book focuses on the grapheme /er/ and is a purple level 8 book band.